PLAYING THE VIOLIN

BOOK TWO

BY CASSIA HARVEY

CHP324

www.charveypublications.com

Cassia Harvey

1.
(Reviewing the A string)

2. The Light Cavalry Overture

Von Suppe, arr. Harvey

3.
(Reviewing the D string)

4. The Daughter of the Regiment

Donizetti, arr. Ambrosio, Harvey

5.

(Reviewing the E string)

6. The Fairy Dance Reel

Trad., arr. Harvey

7.
(Reviewing the G string)

8. The Cows Went Roaring Home

Trad. Latvian, arr. Harvey

Play both strings together (a double stop.)

9.
(Skipping notes)

10. Ocean Hornpipe

Trad., arr. Harvey

11.
(Skipping for Stronger Fingers)

12. Miss Montgomerie's Reel

Trad., arr. Harvey

13.
(Skipping on the D String)

14. Even and Odd

Trad., arr. Harvey

15.

(Low second finger on the E string: G♮)

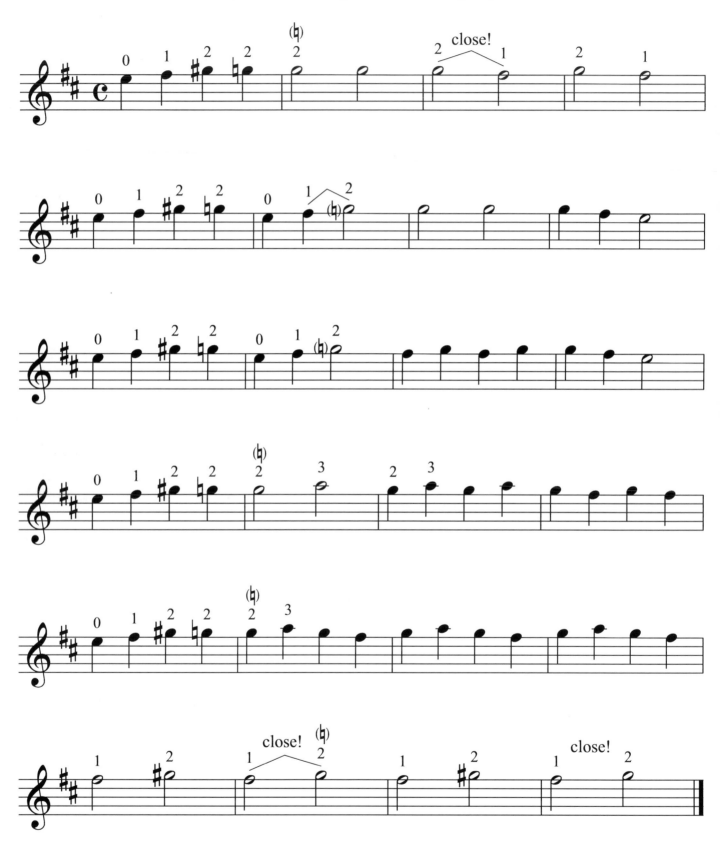

16. Free as a Bird

Trad., arr. Harvey

17.

(Low second finger on the A string: C♮)

18. Radetzky March

Strauss, arr. Harvey

19.
(Low second finger on the D string: F♮)

20. Don Giovanni

Mozart, arr. Harvey

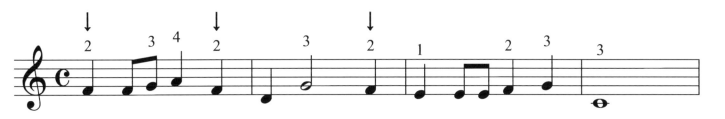

21.
(Back and forth: High 2nd finger and Low 2nd finger)

22. Robin Hood and Little John

Trad., arr. Harvey

23. The Golden Vanity

Trad., arr. Harvey

24.
(Low and High Second Finger)

25. Russian Song

Tchaikovsky, arr. Harvey

26.

(The Key Signature of G major: High and Low 2nd Finger)

27. Poet and Peasant Overture

Von Suppe, arr. Ambrosio, Harvey

28.

(Low Second Finger in D major)

29. Concerto, Op. 3, No. 12

Vivaldi, arr. Harvey

30. Slurs: Playing Two Notes in One Bow

When you get to the middle of your bow, change strings.
Keep moving the bow in the same direction.

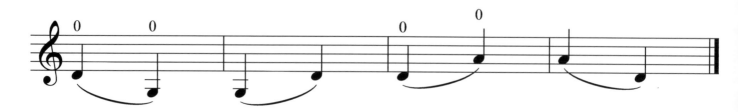

Start by playing the first note.
When you get to the middle of the bow, pick your finger up.

Start by playing the first note. When you get to the middle
of the bow, put your finger down on the string.

Start by playing the first note. When you get to the middle
of the bow, play the next note.

31. Dakota Indian Melody

Trad., arr. Harvey

Slow bow!

32.
(High 3rd Finger on the G string)

33. Yankee Doodle with Variation

Trad., arr. Harvey

34.
(High 3rd Finger on the D string)

close!

35.
(High 3rd Finger on the A string)

close!

36. Marcio Gallop

Trad., arr. Laybourn, Harvey

37. Canon Practice 1

38. Canon Practice 2

39. Pachelbel's Canon

40.
(Playing in C Major)

41. Allegro and Variations

Mozart, Harvey

42.

(C Major Study)

43. Can-Can and Variations

Offenbach, arr. Harvey

Advanced Pieces

44. Mansaniello Quadrille

Trad., arr. Laybourn, Harvey

45. Lancer's Quadrille

Trad., arr. Laybourn, Harvey

46. Spanish Folk Song

Trad., arr. Harvey

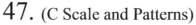

47. (C Scale and Patterns)

48. (Low G Scale and Patterns)

F#

F#

49. (High G Scale and Patterns)

F# and C#

50. (D Scale and Patterns)

51. (A Scale and Patterns)

F♯, C♯, and G♯

52. Fiddle Farewell

Flying Fiddle Duets for Two Violins, Book One

John Ryan's Polka

Trad., arr. Myanna Harvey

Made in the USA
Las Vegas, NV
03 April 2022

46796853R00028